KU-165-604

18
15 8

£2

101
Ways To Improve Your Mind

101
Ways To Improve Your Mind

RACHEL WALKER

Michael O'Mara Books Limited

First published in Great Britain in 2004 by
Michael O'Mara Books Limited
9 Lion Yard, Tremadoc Road
London SW4 7NQ

Copyright © Michael O'Mara Books 2004

All rights reserved. No part of this publication may be reproduced, stored in
a retrieval system, or transmitted by any means, without the prior permission
in writing of the publisher, nor be otherwise circulated in any form of binding
or cover other than that in which it is published and without a similar
condition including this condition being imposed on the subsequent
purchaser.

A CIP catalogue record for this book is available from the British Library.

ISBN 1-84317-129-5

1 3 5 7 9 10 8 6 4 2

Designed and typeset by Envy Design

Printed and bound by Rzeszowskie Zakłady Graficzne S.A., Poland, E.U.

CONTENTS

ACKNOWLEDGEMENTS

My thanks to the following for all their useful tips, help and encouragement in writing this book: Margaret Klein, Gillian Condon, Simon Mattheson, Nicola Williams, Amanda Kilpatrick and Bob Wilson.

INTRODUCTION

As the only animals on this planet who are capable of thinking both creatively and rationally, who have the ability to read and write, and who can comprehend emotion and take meaningful pleasure in life, it seems only fitting that as *homo sapiens* we should strive to use our minds to their fullest potential. That we don't always do so is no doubt a reflection of that other great human trait – laziness – but with the help of this book it is hoped that this imbalance might be redressed.

Generally speaking, when thinking about improving the mind we are in fact considering two different concepts – the physical chemistry of the brain, and the spiritual nature of the mind. Yet, no matter how separate these two areas appear to be, they can, and frequently do, overlap. For instance – by changing our diet it is possible to alter the physical working of our brains as well as affect our mood, and therefore our spirits. Likewise, a good night's sleep will rest the brain, reduce our stress levels and improve our spiritual well-being.

In compiling this book my main aim has been to put together as varied a bag of ideas, tips and information (including nutritional advice, methods of improving the memory, of breaking bad habits, and of overcoming stress and anxiety) as possible, which will help the reader improve both physical brain function and spiritual welfare, and from which they can pick and choose to suit their own needs. I have also included some quizzes and brainteasers, designed to test the reader's mental agility.

Finally, it is also worth noting that the three most powerful tools we have at our disposal in terms of improving mental capacity are simply the desire to learn, the ability to keep an open mind and the dedication to keep going. Without these we are lost and no amount of 'Mind Maps', vitamins or soul-searching are ever likely to help.

Rachel Walker

HEALTH WARNING

None of the herbal remedies suggested in this book should be taken if you are on any other medication and without first consulting your doctor.

A SHORT STRESS TEST

One of the quickest ways to assess the 'condition' of your mental health is to undertake a stress test. Answering the questions below will give you some indication of your stress levels and, should you need it, guide you towards the right kind of help.

Have you recently suffered the loss of a close family member or friend? **Score 100**

Have you recently fallen out with a best friend?
Score 65

Are you caring for an elderly or sick relative? **Score 95**

Have you recently moved house? **Score 80**

Have you recently been divorced or separated from a significant other? **Score 90**

Do you often find yourself crying for no apparent reason?
Score 55

Have you recently suffered from a major illness?
Score 85

Have you recently begun a new job? **Score 60**

Have you recently lost a beloved pet? **Score 35**

Do you find it almost impossible to motivate yourself to get up in the mornings? **Score 25**

Are you suffering from an increased number of arguments with your partner or family?

Score 50

Have you recently become pregnant or given birth, or has your partner recently done either of these things?

Score 70

Has anyone in your family recently suffered from a major illness?

Score 75

Have you noticed a recent change in your sleeping habits?

Score 10

Have you recently been experiencing problems at work – for instance, are you arguing with colleagues or your boss?

Score 85

SCORING

If you have scored between 1 and 150 you are in a low stress category. This is excellent news, but be aware of the symptoms of stress that can creep up at any time.

If you have scored between 150 and 250 you are probably suffering from several stress-related conditions, and you should perhaps consider taking action to address these in the near future.

If you have scored above 250 then you are almost certainly highly stressed and should take immediate action to remedy your condition. To begin with, daily relaxation techniques would be highly beneficial.

NB – if you are feeling desperately low or depressed it is very important that you seek medical advice from your GP as soon as possible.

1

PRACTICE MAKES PERFECT

No one becomes proficient in any skill or profession in life, be they a tennis player, a mathematician, an artist or a scientist, without a great deal of hard work, and, in most cases, a huge amount of practice. Improving your mind is no exception. It requires dedication, a constant willingness to learn and to broaden your horizons, and, in some cases, an entirely different approach to diet and exercise. No one said it would be easy!

You cannot teach a man anything; you can only help him to find it within himself.
GALILEO GALILEI, ITALIAN ASTRONOMER AND PHYSICIST,
1564–1642

2

QUIZ I

Completing riddles and puzzles of all descriptions is an excellent way of keeping the mind on its figurative toes. It isn't important whether you solve them quickly or slowly, but the thought processes involved in trying to work out what at first seems like an impossible problem will begin to open up new neural pathways and encourage you to think from different angles. To get the mental cogs whirring, try solving these riddles.

I am light as a feather, but big as a barn.
Sixty horses can't pull me off the ground.
What am I?

✦

As a whole, I am safe and secure.
Behead me, and I become a place of meeting.
Behead me again, and I am the partner of ready.
Restore me, and I become the domain of beasts.

I'm where yesterday follows today,
And tomorrow's between them.
What am I?

✦

I can run, but not walk.
Wherever I go, thought follows close behind.
What am I?

✦

You are in the room before Heaven and Hell, and leading to each destination is a nondescript door. In front of each door is a talking parrot. One of the parrots always tells the truth; the other always tells a lie. You have no idea which bird is in front of which door. You can ask one of the birds one question to determine correctly the doorway to Heaven. What question do you ask, and to which bird?

✦

A man walks up to you and says, 'Everything I say to you is a lie.'
Is he telling you the truth or is he lying?

(Answers on page 113)

3

GINSENG

'Ginseng soothes base emotions, safeguards the soul, drives out fear, expels evil influences, brightens the eye, opens up the heart, increases the spirit and, if taken over a long period of time, prolongs life.' This quotation is taken from the *Shen Nung Pen Tsao*, China's first pharmacopoeia, which was published more than 2,000 years ago. Nowadays, if not quite a 'miracle drug', ginseng's properties are hailed widely, and are said to include reducing fatigue, stimulating the heart and arteries (which helps the brain access greater levels of oxygen), relaxing the nervous system and calming the mind. In some quarters it is also believed that ginseng can improve the memory, but conclusive evidence for this has yet to be found.

NB – ginseng should not be taken if you are on any other medication and without first consulting your doctor.

4

LEARN ANOTHER LANGUAGE

Travel broadens the mind, but so can learning a new language. Research in Canada has shown that mastering a foreign tongue (to the point where you are bilingual) helps to protect the brain against the onset of age-related diseases such as short- and long-term memory loss. But even if you cannot reach the stage where you are confident with speaking a second language, the benefits of striving towards fluency will improve your capacity to concentrate and to retain information.

5

OILY FISH

Fish, in particular the more oily varieties such as mackerel, salmon, herring, sardines and tuna, have long been associated with a healthy diet. For the most part this is due to the essential omega-3 fatty acids they contain. Societies that eat a high amount of omega-3-rich fish, such as the Inuit (Eskimo) people, have been shown to suffer far less coronary heart disease and arthritis than their European cousins. But the benefits do not stop there. The brain constitutes almost 60 per cent fat, and in order to function properly relies on a steady flow of omega-3s, which have been shown to counteract mood disorders (including mild depression), and regulate more severe mental health problems.

6

BACK-TO-FRONT I

Warming your body up before embarking on any form of strenuous exercise is a well-known technique for avoiding injuries and maintaining good performance, but few of us ever bother to do as much for our brains. Why not try this simple technique?

Pick a number over fifty but under one hundred from which to start, counting backwards in sevens. Once you have reached the lowest number you can, start again, only this time count backwards in fives, eights or sixes. Similarly, try saying the alphabet backwards, or spelling out familiar words back to front. All of these tests will help kick-start your mind and keep it well-oiled throughout the day.

Brain: an apparatus with which we think, we think.
AMBROSE BIERCE, US SATIRIST, SHORT-STORY WRITER AND
JOURNALIST, 1842-1914

7

GARDENING

If you want to be happy for a couple of hours, so the saying goes, then retire to the pub and get drunk. If you want to be happy for a couple of years then walk up the aisle and get married. But if you want to be happy for the rest of your life, ensure you have a small space in which to garden.

Gardening is a wonderful means of stimulating both the mind *and* the body simultaneously. From the smallest window box to the largest country estate, simply being able to grow something from seed, and watch it prosper, flower or bear fruit has been shown to increase a sense of general well-being and lift the spirits. It increases awareness of the movement of the seasons, and our receptivity to the calming effects of nature. In addition, if you can garden and, in the process, grow your own brain foods such as broccoli, spinach and Brussels sprouts, you will have achieved two objectives in one!

8

CALCIUM

Normally, when we think of calcium, it's in relation to our bones and our teeth, but what is not so well known is that it also plays a major role in calming our nerves. A well-balanced diet that includes milk, cheese and nuts is therefore recommended, but other high-calcium foodstuffs that won't immediately spring to mind are spinach, spring greens and a South American grain called quinoa. Quinoa has the added property that, unlike most other grains, it has very low levels of gluten, as well as containing certain amino acids that the body is unable to produce itself, making it a useful addition to the diet.

9

YOGA

Relaxation, in all its forms, is as important to the mind as stimulation, and for hundreds of thousands of people yoga is the ultimate way to unwind. From the Sanskrit word *yug* – 'to yoke' – yoga is literally the binding together of the mind, body and spirit to create a balanced whole. Learning to relax is an art form and takes time to master, so you will need to find a quiet place in which to practise, and set aside at least half an hour each day (preferably early morning) to maximize its effect. Why not join a yoga class and enjoy the company, encouragement and training of those around you?

Which single word will make a new word when added after the first, and will also make a new word when placed in front of the second?

CABBAGE…WORK

(Answer on page 113)

10

SWEET DREAMS

Achieving a good night's sleep is one of the most important ways of ensuring you are in tip-top mental condition. On average, most people need seven to eight hours sleep per night, although certain individuals will require either far less or far more. Sufficient shut-eye is crucial for effective daily function; lack of sleep causes irritability, together with an inability to concentrate, and reduced memory retention. If you are finding it difficult to fall asleep here are some simple tips to help you on your way:

- Ensure that your bed is as comfortable and supportive as possible.
- Cut out common stimulants such as tea and coffee, fizzy drinks with a high caffeine content, and reduce your alcohol intake.
- Try counting backwards from a high number and visualize each number as it passes.
- A warm bath before bedtime, and listening to relaxation tapes, may help to lull you to sleep.

11

POWER WALKING

If you are not one of those people who enjoys putting on trainers and running through the streets of our cities, then a brisk, half-hour walk is a good alternative way to stimulate the body and keep the mind active. In order to benefit truly from this form of exercise, wear loose clothing so your body can 'breathe', swing your arms as you move, take long strides and breathe deeply. In addition, rather than popping down to the shops in the car, why not walk or go by bicycle? Aside from the benefits of brisk exercise, you will feel good about making the decision to use your own two feet.

A weak mind is like a microscope, which magnifies trifling things, but cannot receive great ones.
LORD CHESTERFIELD, ENGLISH STATESMAN AND MAN OF LETTERS,
1694–1773

12

QUIZ 2

You have been asked to assign offices to six staff members. (You have eight staff, but some are not entitled to their own office.) The available offices, numbered 1-6 consecutively, are arranged in a row, and separated only by low dividers. Therefore, voices, sounds, and cigarette smoke readily pass from each office to those on either side. The staff and their requirements are:

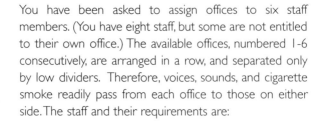

- Jill speaks on the telephone frequently throughout the day.
- Chris and Isabel often talk, and prefer to have adjacent offices.
- Lucy is entitled to office 5, which has the largest window.
- Sally needs silence in the office(s) adjacent to her own.
- John, Andrew and Steve all smoke.
- Lucy must have non-smokers in the office(s) adjacent to her own.

- Unless otherwise specified, all employees maintain silence while in their offices.

1. Which office (1 to 6) is the best location for Chris?

2. Who would be the best employee to occupy the office furthest from Isabel: John, Jill, Lucy, Sally or Andrew?

3. In which of the offices can the three employees who smoke be placed: 1, 2 and 3; 1, 2 and 4; 1, 2 and 6; 2, 3 and 4; 2, 3 and 6?

4. Which of these events, following the assignment of offices, would be most likely to lead to a request for a change in office assignment by one or more employees: Jill decides that she needs silence in the office(s) adjacent to her own; Isabel contracts laryngitis; Sally quits smoking; John takes over the duties formerly assigned to Jill; Lucy decides she wants to play loud music in her office?

(Answers on page 113)

13

KEEP A PET

Keeping a pet (dogs and cats in particular) might not seem the most obvious way to improve the mind, but it certainly has its benefits. Research has shown that stroking animals reduces the heart rate and alleviates stress. Looking after an animal that is totally reliant on you for its well-being increases a sense of responsibility and keeps one alert. For those who live alone, sharing one's home with an animal also brings companionship, which is a very important factor in keeping the mind stimulated. Finally, if you own a dog, with Fido by your side it is far more likely that you will take regular, daily exercise.

14

READ IN THE LOO

Maximizing your mind's potential need never stop – perusing an encyclopaedia, dictionary or book of facts while attending to a call of nature is a great use of 'latent' time, and you'll be surprised at what you remember! Why not try learning a new word, or the capital city of some far-flung kingdom, or the meaning of the word 'serendipity'?

It is good to rub and polish our brain against that of others.
MICHEL DE MONTAIGNE, FRENCH ESSAYIST, 1533–92

15

MUSIC

Music is a wonderful tool with which to stimulate your mind. Research has indicated that not only do foetuses benefit from hearing classical music, but that musicians are more likely to have more of the grey cells in a part of the brain known as Broca's area, which while most commonly associated with language skills, is also involved in comprehending musical structure and composition.

If, however, playing a musical instrument is not for you, then exercising to music has also been shown to aid the brain. For example, verbal processing (and therefore an aptitude for language and comprehension) has been seen to increase after an exercise routine accompanied by Vivaldi's *The Four Seasons*.

Furthermore, musical rhythms have also been proved to affect the heartbeat and alter brainwaves. Music by Mozart has been shown to calm the mind, increase spatial awareness and boost creativity. Jazz music and Gregorian chant have also been revealed to help stimulate the mind and aid the creative process.

16

AROMATHERAPY – HEAVEN SCENT

For centuries it has been acknowledged that scent affects both our mental and physical well-being, and aromatherapy is the practical application of this knowledge. Pure essences, distilled from aromatic plants such as rosemary, lavender, mint, camomile, cedarwood and almond, can be used to stimulate or relax the mind depending on whether one wants to decrease stress or increase alertness. To achieve the desired result, treatment can take the form of an aromatherapy massage, or by burning essential oils.

Other ways of reaping the benefits of aromatherapy are to sprinkle a few drops of essential lavender oil on to your pillow to aid sleep and help the mind wake up refreshed, or apply a few drops of essential lemon-grass oil to the pulse points on the neck, wrists and ankles to revive the spirits.

17

WATER

Water makes up almost 85 per cent of our blood, and as such acts as the body's major transportation system, delivering nutrients, fighting infection, healing wounds and removing waste products. Drinking between six and eight glasses of clean, fresh H_2O will help you to remain alert and aid your concentration on daily tasks. Conversely, a lack of water will cause dehydration that will reduce your energy levels significantly and impair brain function. Lack of water also causes mild depression and it is believed as well that migraines can be triggered due to dehydration. Sip water (preferably bottled) throughout the day.

Music alone with sudden charms can bind
The wand'ring sense, and calm the troubled mind.
WILLIAM CONGREVE, ENGLISH DRAMATIST AND POET, 1670–1729

18

NUTS AND SEEDS

Increasingly, diet has been shown to play a key role in improving IQ levels, and as a result certain foodstuffs, because of their composition, have now become synonymous with the term 'brain food'. These brain foods includes oily fish (see page 11), but also whole grains, nuts and seeds, which are a great source of complex carbohydrates. For instance, almonds make the perfect brain snack as they contain protein, minerals and essential omega-6 fatty acids. Pumpkin seeds are another good source of omega-6, but they have the added bonus of also containing omega-3 oils, which are usually only found in oily fish. On a note of caution, it is important to be aware that nuts can cause allergic reactions, and care should always be taken if you suspect you might be susceptible.

Children use the fist until they are of age
to use the brain.
ELIZABETH BARRETT BROWNING, ENGLISH POET, 1806–1861

19

NOT A CROSS WORD

Just because the brain is not a muscle in the conventional sense, that doesn't mean it won't benefit from rigorous exercise, and to this end crosswords provide an excellent work-out. Quick crosswords will introduce you to words you might not be familiar with, thereby improving your vocabulary, while cryptic crosswords will exercise not only your word power and general knowledge, but also your ability to think laterally. It is no coincidence that the majority of men and women employed at Bletchley Park as code-crackers during the Second World War were mostly excellent 'crossworders'.

20

BRAIN GYMNASTICS

In order to keep your brain functioning at peak efficiency, both the left- and right-hand sides have to be alert at all times. One of the best methods of achieving this is to practise brain gymnastics every morning. A good exercise is as follows.

Begin by standing in a clear space, and swing out sideways your left leg and right arm at the same time. Do the same with your right leg and left arm, and continue this alternating movement until you have completed twenty swings on each side. Next, kick your left leg up behind you and touch your heel with your right hand. Reverse this action with the right leg and the left hand. Finally, swing up your left foot in front of you, and touch your toes with the opposing hand. Twenty alternate repetitions of this will complete the exercise and ensure that both sides of the brain have been galvanized into action, ready for the day.

21

BROCCOLI

Broccoli is one of the finest foods one can eat to keep the mind and body in a healthy condition. Packed full of vitamins and minerals, it is one of the 'free radical' fighting foods that are so good at preventing cancer by protecting the brain, body and nerve cells from oxidative damage. When choosing broccoli always try to pick out the darkest stalks, and, if you are not cooking it straight away, store it in a cool, dark place. Ideally broccoli should only be cooked for a short period of time (preferably by steaming), in order to preserve every last drop of goodness.

A woman has seven children. Half of them are boys. How is this possible?

(Answer on page 114)

22

CONCISE CLASSICS

Naturally, while there is no substitute for being well-read and thereby having at the very least a passing knowledge of the literary classics, sometimes life is too short to read Proust's *À la recherche du temps perdu* or James Joyce's *Ulysses* from beginning to end. Do not despair. There are many websites that handily provide you with plot summaries, character sketches and thematic introductions to popular books. After a swift couple of hours you should then feel confident enough to dazzle your friends with your new-found erudition. Alternatively, many works of literature, poetry and autobiography are available on CD and tape, to which you can listen before going to bed, or while on a journey. If your conscience pricks you, consider it as an introduction for when you find the time to read the entire work…

23

QUIZ 3

A little spider is trapped in a bath that is 40 inches deep. Every day, the spider climbs up 10 inches, but every morning the owner of the bath takes a shower and the spider slips backwards 8 inches. How many frustrating days does it take the spider to get out of the bath? **a**. 9; **b**. 16; **c**. 20; **d**. 27

Five-year-old Charlie wanted to buy his mum a red rose for her birthday, and so he decided to start saving on the first day of the month. On the first day, he put one pence in his piggy bank, on the second day he put two pence, on the third day three pence and so on. By the day of her birthday, he had saved up £3.00 – exactly the correct amount to buy the red rose. On what day of the month did her birthday fall? **a.** 13th; **b.** 19th; **c.** 24th; **d.** 30th

(Answers on page 114)

24

THE INTERNET

We are living in the Information Age, a time in which the Internet plays a prominent role. Sadly, hours can be wasted surfing through pages and pages of unedifying rubbish. A careful trawl, however, will provide the user with online dictionaries that will email you the 'Word of the Day', news and broadcasting services supplying breaking news, and reference providers sending the 'Fact of the Day'. Make the knowledge come to you.

Grace had it first. Morag had it last. Virginia Lemming had it twice until she married Robert Brown.
What is it?

(Answer on page 114)

25

BACK-TO-FRONT 2

On page 12 I suggested you try a simple technique for warming up the mind by counting backwards in sevens, or by saying the alphabet backwards. Another slightly more complicated version of this game is to recite the times-tables backwards, beginning with the tens and ending with the twos. This takes immense concentration, but if done every morning should help your brain remain keen and focused.

If I had to live my life again I would have made a rule to read some poetry and listen to some music at least once a week; for perhaps the parts of my brain now atrophied could thus have been kept active through use.

CHARLES DARWIN, ENGLISH NATURALIST, 1809–82

26

NO SMOKING PLEASE

Although the benefits of giving up smoking normally focus on how it will improve your physical well-being, there are benefits to your mind, too. First and foremost, smoking reduces the brain's oxygen supply, so quitting will immediately boost your brain's capacity to 'breathe'. Secondly, smoking depletes all of the B vitamins in your body (which are vital for mental energy) and increases the need for vitamin C in order to protect the brain from free radicals that can contribute to organ damage.

Also, contrary to popular opinion, smoking increases stress levels rather than alleviating them. Although giving up might be stressful in itself, the long-term benefits to your mental health will be significant. Finally, no one likes to smell like an old ashtray, and by giving up you will have a more positive self-image and feel more confident when leaning in for a kiss!

Tips for quitting:

- Consult with your local health centre – often they will run give-up-smoking help clinics.
- Try the nicotine-replacement therapies on offer, such as the gum or the patches, until you find one that works for you.
- If you can, brush your teeth every time you crave a cigarette – that way you can savour your clean, fresh breath and remind yourself why you wanted to quit in the first place.

*A collection of a hundred great brains
makes one big fathead.*
CARL GUSTAV JUNG, SWISS PSYCHOLOGIST, 1875–1961

27

BETA-CAROTENE

Foods that are rich in beta-carotene (which the body converts to vitamin A – an essential antioxidant), such as carrots, sweet potatoes and the majority of dark green vegetables, are essential for good brain maintenance. Sweet potatoes in particular are full of antioxidants as well as vitamins C and E. However, for the highest levels of beta-carotene, choose the darkest yellow, youngest specimens and avoid older, drier ones at all costs.

28

LAUGHTER

Laughter is a wonderful means of relieving stress and combating that most debilitating of conditions, depression. In the film *Hannah and Her Sisters*, when Woody Allen believes he is suffering from a terminal illness he goes in search of the meaning to life, only to end up in a cinema watching a Marx Brothers film. Laughter lowers the blood pressure, boosts the immune system and releases endorphins, which are the body's natural painkiller. It has also been shown that laughter stimulates both the left- and right-hand sides of the brain, thus enhancing our learning abilities. Smiles help us connect with people and therefore enable us to enjoy our lives and relationships to the full.

29

GLUCOSE

Glucose is the brain's favourite fuel. In order to perform satisfactorily throughout the day the brain must receive a constant and regular flow of this sugar. Fast-releasing carbohydrates are to be avoided at all costs (for example, white sugar, white bread, sweets, biscuits and cakes) as they break down into glucose very quickly and flood the brain rather than drip-feed it. As a result, although you will receive an initial 'high' after drinking a fizzy soft drink, this surge of energy will often be followed by a dramatic 'low', leading to a decreased attention span and acute irritability. The best source of glucose is complex, slow-releasing carbohydrate such as brown rice, fruit, vegetables, wholewheat pasta, and porridge oats.

The greatest discovery of my generation is that man can alter his life simply by altering his attitude of mind.
WILLIAM JAMES, US PHILOSOPHER AND PYCHOLOGIST, 1842–1910

30

ACUPUNCTURE

The ancient art of acupuncture is Chinese in origin and involves the treatment of illness and improvement of well-being by inserting the thinnest of needles into selected acupuncture points on the body. Acupuncture has its basis in the fact that the Chinese believe that true health can only be achieved through the balance of opposing forces, i.e. the *yin* (spirit/mind), and the *yang* (blood/body). When these are working in harmony they create an energy flow, or *chi*, which moves through the body along meridian lines. 'No pain, no blockage; no blockage, no pain' runs the acupuncture axiom – when the flow of chi is blocked, our health suffers. The application of needles at prescribed acupoints is a means by which a trained practitioner clears the blockage and restores one's good health. It has been widely speculated that acupuncture alters the flow of blood to the brain and in so doing releases certain chemicals, such as serotonin, which is vital in the fight against depression.

31

TOMATOES

Tomatoes are another of the brain's natural white knights. Containing high levels of lycopene (responsible for giving tomatoes their red colour, and also thought to be a key antioxidant), tomatoes act as a powerful means of protecting the brain and nervous system. Tomatoes also contain several key B vitamins and minerals, which help to produce and protect the brain's neuromessengers.

The freshest and healthiest tomatoes are the reddest fruits, as these will contain the highest levels of vitamin C and lycopene. Even tinned tomatoes have health benefits for they also contain vitamin C – approximately two-thirds of the amount in the fresh variety – which is better than nothing.

32

QUIZ 4

Because riddles are such a clever way of making your brain tackle relatively complicated problems, here are a few more for you to solve.

Runs smoother than any rhyme,
Loves to run but cannot climb.
What is it?

✦

Goes to the door and doesn't knock,
Goes to the window and doesn't rap,
Goes to the fire and doesn't warm,
Goes upstairs and does no harm.
What is it?

✦

How far can a dog run into the woods?

I never was, am always to be
No one ever saw me, nor ever will,
And yet I am the confidence of all
To live and breathe on this terrestrial ball.
What am I?

+

We are little creatures;
All of us have different features.
One of us in glass is set
One of us you'll find in jet.
Another you may see in tin,
And the fourth is boxed within
If the fifth you should pursue,
It can never fly from you.
What are we?

(Answers on page 114)

33

POLLYANNA

Pollyanna might not be your ideal role model, but the girl with the braids and freckles did understand the benefits of positive thinking.

These days it is all too easy to fear the future, expect failure, see the bad in every situation, criticize yourself, doubt your own abilities and, as a result, feel depressed and incapable of functioning normally. But negative thoughts should be challenged at every opportunity and one of the simplest ways to do this is to think of reasons to be cheerful, even in the bleakest of situations. Counting your blessings is a simple, yet effective, way of combating the most disabling of thoughts, and of helping you to regain a positive outlook.

34

LEAN MEAT

In order to supply the brain with all the equipment required to manufacture neurotransmitters (those chemicals that relay messages from cell to cell) we require a constant supply of amino acids, which are most commonly found in protein foods such as meat and fish. Lean, white meat such as fresh chicken and turkey is probably best as these are both lower in fat than beef or lamb. It is also advisable to buy organically produced meat wherever possible, as this will not contain steroid hormones or large amounts of antibiotics.

The brain is a wonderful organ. It starts working the moment you get up in the morning and does not stop until you get into the office.
ROBERT FROST, US POET, 1874–1963

35

BLACKSTRAP MOLASSES

The popularity of blackstrap molasses (a thick, dark, syrupy-type substance) has declined over recent years which is a shame because, unlike its kissing cousin white sugar, blackstrap molasses is a brain food par excellence. For instance, two tablespoonfuls of this black liquid-gold contains three times more iron than an egg and considerably more calcium than a glass of milk! Molasses is also a rich source of B vitamins, as well as minerals such as magnesium, copper and manganese.

In winter, molasses makes the perfect comfort drink when a few spoonfuls are added to boiling water. Or you could add a little to stews and soups or to cake mixtures as an alternative to sugar.

36

T'AI CHI

Like yoga, t'ai chi is an excellent way of dealing with tension and of relaxing the mind. Simply speaking, it is a form of meditation characterized by extremely slow movements of the arms, head and legs which tend to follow the forms of karate or kung fu, but which are practised at a much slower pace. These motions are said to improve stamina, increase the internal circulation, and deepen the breathing. The relaxation techniques of t'ai chi are balanced by a martial-arts element, but thankfully for most people in the Western world it is not compulsory to master the more rigorous aspects of the discipline to benefit from its healing potential!

Regular practice of t'ai chi will help maintain the harmony between body and mind, and will encourage belief in your ability to moderate your behaviour and attitudes, both mentally and physically.

37

CUT DOWN ON CAFFEINE

Caffeine, which is most commonly found in everyday drinks such as coffee, tea and most fizzy soft drinks, is a menace to brain function. It interferes with the effectiveness of iron, potassium, zinc, calcium and vitamin B1 – all needed for the smooth running of messages to and from the brain.

Caffeine also promotes insomnia, anxiety and depression, so it makes good sense either to avoid it altogether or at the very least cut down on your consumption of drinks that contain caffeine.

38

KNITTING

In recent years knitting has enjoyed a renaissance, and, taken up by the stars as the pastime of choice, it is now seen as cool to wield a ball of wool and two needles! But there are more significant benefits to knitting than being perceived as trendy. As with any manual task which involves hand/eye coordination, a half-hour with the needles will exercise the brain and keep your mind agile. Following patterns also exercises the mind, but you don't have to be an expert knitter to benefit from this craft. Simply by knitting a scarf or a hat you will be putting your brain to good use, and you'll be saving yourself money at the same time!

Ideas must work through the brains and arms of men,
or they are no better than dreams.
RALPH WALDO EMERSON, US POET,
ESSAYIST AND PHILOSOPHER, 1803–1882

39

LIVER

Unfortunately, liver is not to everyone's taste, but if you do like it or can persuade yourself to eat some, it is of enormous benefit. Rich in protein, liver is also packed full of the type of nutrients that are essential in the fight against stress. For instance, liver contains large amounts of vitamin B5 which is one of the top-scoring anti-stress vitamins. Liver also contains folic acid and vitamins B2, B3 and B12 – all of which provide energy for the brain, as do high quantities of iron, also found in liver, which aids mental alertness. Lamb's liver is, in most cases, a better option than either chicken or calf's liver for top-notch nutrition and, as always, organically produced meat is better than the ordinary kind.

The mind is its own place, and in itself
Can make a heaven of hell, a hell of heaven.
(Paradise Lost)
JOHN MILTON, ENGLISH POET, 1608–1674

40

AEROBIC EXERCISE

Aerobic exercise is the perfect way to increase your cardiovascular endurance, by pushing the muscles to draw on oxygen in the blood. This will decrease blood pressure, strengthen your heart, improve your immune system, and increase your stamina – all of which will mean you'll feel happier about your body. It has also been shown that aerobic exercise promotes the release of the body's endorphins, which are natural sedatives that help stabilize mood swings.

What word or expression is depicted below?

amUous

(Answer on page 114)

41

REMEMBERING LISTS

No one's memory is perfect, but help is at hand. Tony Buzan, who invented 'Mind Maps' also has several solutions to the memory problem, including this simple technique for remembering lists.

As an example, take a shopping list that includes milk, tomatoes, butter, bread, chicken and cat food. The simplest way to remember this is to make up a story involving each of the items. For instance: on your way to the shops you see a cow outside your house, after which you pass by a cottage with tomato plants growing out of a huge, old-fashioned butter churn. Through the window of the cottage wafts the smell of freshly baked bread. You continue on your walk only to see a car narrowly avoiding a chicken that is being chased by a huge ginger cat. Creating a narrative in this way helps to put the shopping-list items into a context and thus makes them much easier to remember.

42

MEDITATION

Practised by many of the great Eastern religions, including Buddhism and Hinduism, as a way of heightening insight into the self and the world, meditation has also been taken up in the West as a means of relieving stress and of strengthening mental reserves and self-discipline.

To establish a meditative frame of mind, find a quiet, calm place in which to sit comfortably. Focus on either a one-syllable word, or perhaps a candle, and take several deep breaths to release the chaos of daily thought, and to focus your attention within. There are many different meditation exercises that you can perform at this stage; perhaps the simplest is just to extend your deep breathing, imagining that with each inward breath you are absorbing the peace of the spiritual universe, and that each outward breath is expelling your worries and anxieties.

If practised regularly, meditation will improve not only your peace of mind, but also your creativity, energy levels, and productivity, too. It really is the complete mental-health kit.

43

VITAMIN C

Vitamin C is one of the body's best weapons in the fight against a whole raft of diseases, but in relation to the brain it is particularly important as a synthesizing component of neurotransmitters, which are critical (ultimately) to clearer thinking. Neurotransmitters have also been shown to affect mood, and therefore a daily intake of vitamin C will help regulate your mental well-being and reduce your stress levels.

To take full advantage of vitamin C, the best natural sources are citrus fruits (i.e. grapefruits, oranges, lemons) as well as blackcurrants, strawberries, red peppers, tomatoes and broccoli. The camu-camu, or bayberry fruit, has the highest concentration of vitamin C in the world; over sixty times that of an orange. Alternatively, you could try taking a vitamin C supplement – available at all chemists and health-food shops.

It is sweet to let the mind unbend on occasion.
HORACE, ROMAN POET AND SATIRIST, 65–8 BC

QUIZ 5

Like riddles, brainteasers are good for tweaking the mind.

You are on an island in the middle of a deep lake. The lake is in a remote northern part of the country and there has never been a bridge connecting the island to the mainland. Every day a tractor and wagon gives hay rides around the island. Puzzled as to how the tractor had arrived on the island, you ask the locals and discover that the tractor was not transported to the island by boat or by air. Nor was it built on the island. How did the tractor get there?

Glenn and Jason each have a collection of cricket balls. Glenn said that if Jason were to give him eight of his balls they would have an equal number; but if Glenn were to give Jason eight of his balls, Jason would have three times as many balls as Glenn. How many balls does Jason have?

(Answers on page 114)

45

BEETROOT

Beetroot is packed full of brain nutrients. The brain requires both carbohydrates and oxygen; beetroot is a rich source of the former and is also loaded with iron, which helps the blood transport oxygen to the brain. In addition, beetroot contains high levels of anthocyanidins (hence the dark purple colouring), which are antioxidants and have anti-inflammatory properties. Finally, beetroot is a rich source of minerals such as potassium, sodium, calcium and phosphorus, all of which help the brain to build more reliable neural connections – i.e. help us to think.

Fresh beetroot is *always* best so try to avoid the pickled variety, which will be depleted of all the above vital nutrients.

46

TAKE A PHOTOGRAPH

We have all at some time or another forgotten where we've left our car keys, put a book down and been unable to relocate it, or found ourselves searching everywhere for our mobile phones. An easy way to remember where we've left things is to take a mental photograph of their location and of nearby objects when we put them down.

So, next time you need to remember where your car keys are, close your eyes and recall your 'photograph'.

Think of a 'powerful' nine-letter English word that contains a single vowel.

(Answer on page 115)

47

ALEXANDER TECHNIQUE

Although commonly associated with improving posture, shedding excess tension and slowing down physical decline, the Alexander Technique is equally good at improving the mind's ability to cope with stress. Named after Frederick Matthias Alexander, an Austrian actor, the technique, which involves 'unlearning' ingrained ideas and 'disengaging' old habits, can relieve a number of mind-related problems such as migraines, insomnia, mild depression and hypertension. In order to gain the most from this technique, however, it is strongly recommended that the reader attends a class or a one-to-one session with a fully trained practitioner.

It is the mind that makes the body rich.
WILLIAM SHAKESPEARE, ENGLISH PLAYWRIGHT AND POET,
1564–1616

48

SERENDIPITY

According to *Chambers Twentieth-Century Dictionary*, serendipity is the 'faculty of making happy chance finds'. First coined by the author Horace Walpole in his fairytale *The Three Princes of Serendip*, whose heroes were constantly making chance discoveries of things 'they were not in quest of', serendipity – in its simplest form – is the art of keeping an open mind.

For example, Sir Alexander Fleming discovered penicillin when a chance spore of mould landed in one of his petri dishes, killing all the bacteria within it. Rather than throwing the dish away and marking the incident down as a failed experiment, Fleming recognized that this was a significant development, which ultimately, with the help of other scientists, led to the mass production of the world's most widely used antibiotic – penicillin. The moral of this story? Always have an open mind.

49

BEANS

Beans, such as red beans, black beans and soy beans, are a valuable source of protein, particularly if you are vegetarian. They also provide a rich supply of minerals such as magnesium, zinc, iron and manganese – all of which are required to work alongside the amino acids to produce and maintain our brain's messaging functions. Finally, beans are a treasure trove of carbohydrates, which are constantly needed to keep the brain properly fuelled.

A note of caution, however: do not eat raw beans (in particular red and soy beans) as these contain harmful toxins which are destroyed by cooking – and always consult the manufacturer's instructions about preparation.

50

RHYME

Writing poetry is often a wonderful way to remember something important. For instance your cousin's birthday falls on 25 July, but you can never remember this date, so you could make something up along these lines:

> Remember, remember July twenty-fifth:
> Time to buy cousin a great birthday gift.

There is a common English word consisting of nine letters, which, each time you remove a letter from it, still remains an English word – from nine letters right down to a single letter. What is the original nine-letter word, and what are the words that it becomes after removing one letter at a time?

(Answer on page 115)

51

SENSORY DEPRIVATION

Sensory-deprivation tanks were all the rage in the eighties and nineties, and although they are used less frequently today, they are still a useful tool for promoting relaxation and mental well-being.

Normal practice involves laying prone in a tank of skin-temperature, heavily salted water, at which point the lid is closed and you remain, floating, in the darkness. This allows the mind to recuperate and relax, free from outside stimuli. Obviously, it is not recommended to anyone who suffers from claustrophobia, but it can be an interesting and unusual experience.

You'll never plough a field by turning it over in your mind.
IRISH PROVERB

52

NO TO FAT

Calorie-dense, fatty foods such as butter, full-fat milk, cream, as well as fried foods, are not just bad for your weight, but they also radically deplete the number of dopamine receptors in the brain, which are powerful neurotransmitters responsible for memory and mood.

Try replacing full-fat milk with skimmed milk, cream with crème fraiche and butter with olive oil or margarine. It is also preferable to eat fish or white meat such as chicken rather than red meat, which contains lots of saturated fat.

My own brain is to me the most unaccountable of machinery – always buzzing, humming, soaring, roaring, diving and then buried in mud. And why? What's this passion for?

VIRGINIA WOOLF, ENGLISH NOVELIST, CRITIC AND ESSAYIST,

1882–1941

53
QUIZ 6

Test your word power with this quiz – match the word that best resembles the relationship between the other two words.

For example: portrait is to picture as _____ is to book.
– ethnography, biography, autobiography, novel
Answer: biography

1. Assimilation is to melting pot as multiculturalism is to _____ . – diversify, homogeneous, mosaic, bilingual

2. Contact lenses are to glasses as ballpoint pen is to _____ . – pencil, fountain pen, marker, ink

3. Sweat is to shiver as _____ is to hungry. – satiated, full, salivate, famished

4. Vest is to undershirt as _____ is to necklace.
 – chain, beads, locket, gold

5. Reptile is to vertebrate as pie is to _____ .
 – meal, dessert, fruit, sweet

6. Applause is to performance as _____ is to book.
 – epilogue, summary, critic, review

7. Lager is to ale as cola is to _____ .
 – juice, coke, root beer, water

8. Hair is to stubble as potatoes are to _____ .
 – french fries, sweet potatoes, potato skins, vegetable

9. Brake is to stop as student is to _____ .
 – read, study, learn, write exams

10. Jingle is to corporation as _____ is to politician.
 – campaign, platform, slogan, promises

(Answers on page 115)

54

CHESS

Playing chess is an ideal method of exercising the mind while relaxing in the comfort of your own home, or indeed, any place you lay down your board. Chess requires the players to plan ahead constantly. They must also hold in mind a great deal of visual information and analyse the consequences of their potential moves and countermoves as well as those of their opponent. Consequently, the game is an ideal way of improving one's decision-making skills as well as improving the memory and capacity to read and react to complex situations. And, of course, it's a wonderful game to challenge your family and friends to.

55

TENNIS

To help improve not only your physical fitness, but also your mental alertness, exercise is an excellent way of shifting your mind away from unpleasant thoughts. Tennis is a great example – it lowers your blood pressure, burns calories and reduces stress. After all, who can forget the Swedish iceberg, Bjorn Borg, who was famous not only for winning several Grand Slam titles but also for his cool, calm demeanour both on and off the court? (It has been said that Borg's resting heart rate was 45 beats per minute – the male average being 70.)

Tennis also improves hand/eye coordination, which in turn benefits that part of the brain that controls movement and spatial awareness. However, as with all the exercises recommended in this book, medical advice should be sought before committing yourself to any strenuous activity if you have any doubts about your fitness levels.

56

THINKING OUTSIDE THE BOX

Generally speaking, 'thinking outside the box' is the ability to think creatively, beyond our innate mental conditioning, towards solutions and ideas not immediately obvious.

For instance, how long does it take you to make sense of the following conundrum?

A father and son are driving along a busy motorway when their vehicle is involved in a head-on collision. The father is killed instantly, but his son is rushed to hospital for a life-saving operation. The surgeon comes down to check on the patient, takes one look at the boy and says, 'I can't operate. That's my son.'

'Thinking outside the box' gives us fresh perspectives on routine tasks and permits us openness to new experiences. Try it!

(Answer on page 115)

57

BRIDGE

The card game bridge is normally associated with older members of society, being what some might call a 'passive' pastime. But nothing could be further from the truth because, as all card players know, to be a good bridge player requires an excellent visual memory and therefore a high level of brain function. Why not join a bridge club and enjoy the company of like-minded others as well as the game itself?

The mind can make
Substance, and people planets of its own
With beings brighter than have been, and give
A breath to forms which can outlive all flesh.
('The Dream')
GEORGE GORDON, LORD BYRON, ENGLISH POET, 1788–1824

58

THAI MASSAGE

Because it not only involves yoga but also acupressure, reflexology and meditation, Thai massage is one of the most wonderful ways of realigning the energies of your body, improving your blood circulation and allowing your mind to relax fully.

Working along the body's pressure points and over its energy fields – a typical Thai massage does not (like the more traditional Western massages) concentrate on the manipulation of individual parts of the body, but instead takes a more holistic and therapeutic approach. Recipients will have their backs walked on, spines bent and stretched, and fingers and toes cracked. A Thai massage increases flexibility, readjusts the skeletal structure, and relieves muscular tension. It will also make you feel very good!

59

MEMORIZING POETRY

Being able to recite poetry from memory will not only impress your friends, but it will also improve your mind. You can learn by rote, but perhaps an easier way to recall your favourite lines is by using visual imagery – and in this instance the more unusual, grotesque and vivid the image, the better.

> *O, what can ail thee knight at arms*
> *Alone and palely loitering?*
> *The sedge has withered from the lake,*
> *And no birds sing!*
>
> JOHN KEATS, 'LA BELLE DAME SANS MERCI'

Perhaps you could summarize this wonderful verse with the following list of pictures, each recalling the line to which they relate:

> A knight in armour armed with a sword
> Standing alone with an extremely pale face
> Amongst a pile of dead weeds
> With birds that have had their beaks removed!

60

CHOCOLATE

Although not every health professional would agree, the great majority of people believe that chocolate is a great way of boosting your mood. During the consumption of top-quality chocolate, the body releases both serotonin and endorphins, both of which help relax the mind and brighten your mood. Also, depending on the grade, chocolate can be a good source of iron, zinc, magnesium, calcium and potassium, all vital for proper brain function. 'Moderation' might be an applicable word here, however!

61

EATING BREAKFAST

Breakfast has long been referred to as the most important meal of the day, and not without good reason. Crucially, it allows you to refuel your body and restock your depleted energy levels after they have run low overnight. Without breakfast, the body has to draw on energy reserves it often doesn't have, which in turn releases stress hormones that will leave you irritable and tired. Try eating wholemeal bread, porridge, freshly-squeezed orange juice, fresh fruit and boiled/poached eggs, and avoid things such as coffee or fried foods.

Iron rusts from disuse; stagnant water loses its purity and in cold weather becomes frozen; even so does inaction sap the vigour of the mind.

LEONARDO DA VINCI, ITALIAN PAINTER, SCULPTOR, ARCHITECT AND ENGINEER, 1452–1519

62

OTHERHANDEDNESS

Without regular mental challenges the brain can become lazy, so why not set it a few hurdles to overcome? Use your 'other' hand to try to brush your teeth, open a can of food or write a letter (though perhaps not all at the same time!). With enough practice, ambidexterity could be within your grasp!

Think of a seven-letter word that doesn't include any of the five vowels.

(Answer on page 115)

63

QUIZ 7

Try the following word games.

Think of words in which four consecutive letters appear in correct alphabetical order in each word: **a.** ABCD; **b.** DEFG; **c.** FGHI; **d.** HIJK; **e.** MNOP; **f.** RSTU.

✦

Think of an English word that contains the letter 'i' six times, and none of the other four vowels.

✦

What expression is this?
THE FAREDCE

✦

What's the one-word answer to this anagram?
A GRIM ERA

✦

What expression is depicted below?
AGB

(Answers on page 115)

64

SOY

In recent years soy's star has been in the ascendant with regards to improving the memory – particularly for menopausal women. Natural plant oestrogens – isoflavones – found in soy products are thought to act on oestrogen receptacles in the brain's hippocampus, the area responsible for memory retention. Soy is also thought to act as a powerful antioxidant, which helps to maintain healthy brain tissue, and, because it is high in protein (but low in fat), it can also help to lower cholesterol levels.

Soy can be included in the diet in a number of ways, but perhaps the easiest is to drink soy milk every couple of days.

65

IRON

Iron is crucial for effective brain function. A lack of this mineral will result in low haemoglobin levels which reduces the flow of oxygen to the brain. Iron can be found in a variety of fresh foods, including red meat, liver, leafy green vegetables (spring greens, spinach and watercress), molasses and whole grains. For optimum efficiency iron requires vitamin C before it is absorbed into the body, so that's another good reason to eat plenty of fruit…

The mind is like a parachute. It only works when it is open.
ANONYMOUS

66

'THERE'S ROSEMARY, THAT'S FOR REMEMBRANCE'

It is unlikely that Shakespeare, in penning this immortal phrase, was referring to improving the memory – however, essential oils made up with both rosemary and sage are thought to be capable of stimulating the brain's recall capacity, as well as increasing vocabulary.

Try sprinkling a few drops in your bath, or on your pillow at night.

I like nonsense; it wakes up the brain cells.
DR SEUSS, US CHILDREN'S WRITER AND CARTOONIST, 1904–91

67

BLACKBERRIES AND BLUEBERRIES

Two other foods that are exceptionally high in antioxidants, and therefore are a tremendous way of fighting disease and keeping the brain fit are blackberries and blueberries. Recently declared the age-busting fruits of the twenty-first century, these small black gems are delicious when freshly sprinkled over cereal. In autumn, and if you are fortunate enough to live in or near the countryside, there is nothing more satisfying than walking down the lanes picking a basketful of blackberries.

Canned and frozen alternatives are also high in antioxidants so for once don't be afraid of getting out the tin-opener!

68

SAUNAS

Taking a sauna might seem an out-of-place suggestion in a book about improving your mind, but as well as detoxifying the body, if used regularly saunas will increase your cardiovascular strength and thereby improve the blood supply to the brain. A sauna is also a wonderful stress-buster, opening and cleansing your pores and improving your mood. In fact, there are few other ways more successful in relieving tension and soothing nerves, so if you don't have the luxury of owning one, why not retire to your local health spa or leisure centre and treat yourself to a sauna today?

The Brain is deeper than the sea –
For – hold them – Blue to Blue –
The one the other will absorb –
As Sponges – Buckets – do –
EMILY DICKINSON, US POET, 1830–1886

69

GINKGO BILOBA

Often referred to as the 'smart pill' because of its memory-enhancing properties, ginkgo biloba comes from one of the oldest tree species (the maidenhair) known to man. The Chinese have used ginkgo biloba for more than 3,000 years for a variety of therapeutic reasons, and, in the West, although not 100 per cent proven, it is thought that the ingestion of ginkgo biloba supplements can improve concentration, enhance mental alertness, benefit the memory and improve mood. Recent studies also suggest that ginkgo biloba might be useful in the fight against Alzheimer's disease, although this research is still in its early stages.

NB – ginkgo biloba should not be taken if you are on any other medication and not without consulting your doctor.

70

NOTE-TAKING

Anyone who is familiar with tennis, and in particular with the Williams sisters, will be aware that Serena Williams often takes notes on court to read during the match. The notes are said to contain tips to keep her mind fixed on the job in hand. Using notecards when you are faced with a stressful situation (such as giving a speech) is a wonderful way to keep your mind focused and to remember key points at crucial moments.

Bodily decay is gloomy in prospect, but of all human contemplations the most abhorrent is body without mind.

THOMAS JEFFERSON, THIRD US PRESIDENT, 1743–1826

71

LECITHIN

Lecithin is a fat-like material that is produced naturally by the liver if you are on a well-balanced diet. Needed by every cell in the body, it is also an essential requirement for the upkeep of the membrane that surrounds and protects the brain. Lecithin granules can be found in most good health-food shops.

While shopping on holiday in Brussels, Louise bought twelve boxes of Belgian chocolates costing 7 Euros each. She handed over a 100-Euro note and added the change to her purse, which already contained seven 50-Euro notes and seven 1-Euro coins. After buying four tickets to a show, which cost her 33 Euros per ticket, how much did she have left over?

(Answer on page 115)

72

MIND RELAXATION

While similar to meditation, mind relaxation is simpler and needs somewhat less practice before reaping results. Lie down on your back in a quiet, warm space and close your eyes. Think of yourself in a calm, pleasant place such as a wooded area, by the sea, or next to a river. Take a walk through that imaginary space and while you do so listen to the wind in the trees, or the waves breaking over the sand, and visualize the flowers and birds. Do not worry if your mind wanders, simply bring it back by gently focusing on an object such as a rock or plant or hill. If you practise this technique every day it will become easier each time to slip into your own piece of Heaven.

73

SAY NO TO WORRY

Worry is one of the most debilitating of mental conditions and is self-replicating – worrying about your worries makes them worse. Useful strategies for dealing with worry are therefore an important part of your psychological armoury. One excellent way of facing down your gremlins is to imagine yourself as a traffic policeman. The moment a worry pops into your head, mentally hold up your hand or a STOP sign to indicate that you will not countenance such a thing. Alternatively, worries often seem less threatening and easier to deal with when they are written down on a piece of paper. Once they are there in black and white you can then draw up a list of ways in which to approach your problems head-on. Don't be afraid to consult your GP if you feel that your worries are getting out of hand.

74

AVOCADOS

If is often said that avocados contain unhealthily high levels of fat, but this is an unfair accusation as what is not mentioned is that this fat is monounsaturated and therefore not the type that clogs up your arteries. In fact, avocados have many cognitive-health benefits due to their high levels of vitamins C, E and A, all of which are powerful antioxidants, and protect the brain from damaging free radicals brought on by stress.

I think we're very early in the evolutionary scale. We don't use a fraction of our brains yet. To be honest, mine is on economy some days.
KYLIE MINOGUE, AUSTRALIAN PERFORMER, 1968–

75

QUIZ 8

How many ways can you read BRAIN in this diamond, using only letters adjacent to each other, in any direction?

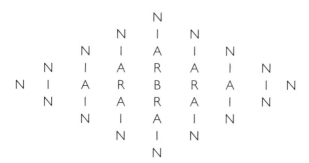

```
                    N
                N   I   N
            N   I   A   I   N
        N   I   A   R   A   I   N
    N   I   A   R   B   R   A   I   N
        N   I   A   R   A   I   N
            N   I   A   I   N
                N   I   N
                    N
```

(Answer on page 116)

76

MNEMONICS

'Never Eat Shredded Wheat' and 'Richard Of York Gained Battles In Vain' are both mnemonics devised to remember specific information – in the first instance the points of the compass, and in the second the colours of the rainbow. Indeed, mnemonics are especially good if you want to remember a list of objects or a sequence of events, and to assist you they can easily be tailored to your specific interests.

Men are not prisoners of fate, but prisoners of their own minds.
FRANKLIN D. ROOSEVELT, THIRTY-SECOND US PRESIDENT,
1882–1945

77

KEEP UP TO DATE

Not only useful for impressing your friends with your vast contemporary knowledge, being well-informed about current affairs will grease the wheels of your professional interaction, too. Buy a daily newspaper (preferably a broadsheet rather than a tabloid), and familiarize yourself with local, national and international events. Also, acquaint yourself with the names and faces of the world leaders and the positions they hold in their respective fields. Rather than watching soap repeats, following news broadcasts either on radio or television will also keep you up to speed with developments in the world. Remember, knowledge is power…

78

'THINK OF A ROOM...'

Use this technique for remembering lists of specific items, or tasks that need to be done – again, using mental imagery. Picture a sparsely decorated imaginary living room, with a large coffee table in the centre, a fireplace to one side, an armchair, a bookcase and a furry rug on the floor. For the sake of this example, you need to remember to pick up your car from the garage, drop your shoes off at the cobblers, and buy a new lead for your dog. You walk into your room and make straight for the bookcase where you see a large glossy car manual. You take this off the shelf, sit down in the armchair and put your feet up on the coffee table to admire your shoes. Finally, before you leave the room, you pick up your rug to shake it out. The texture of the rug is as soft as your dog's fur.

79

REDUCE YOUR ALCOHOL INTAKE

We are all aware of the debilitating effect of alcohol on our bodies, but what we may not be so conscious of is the damage it does to our brain. Although red wine, in moderation, is believed in some circles to have a small positive effect on health, generally the news is not good. Heavy and regular alcohol consumption affects the working memory (which damages long-term recall), and can increase the likelihood of seizures, depression, anxiety and stress. It also lingers in the body for longer than is perceived, affecting concentration, precision and mood. Add to this the embarrassing or dangerous things that you can do while drunk, and it's clear that too much alcohol is no friend of a healthy mind. Try reducing the frequency with which you drink, consuming water while drinking alcohol (and afterwards), and try to cut back on the number of drinks you'll have in an evening. You'll get a better night's sleep, too.

80

POWER NAPS

Both Margaret Thatcher and Thomas Edison were renowned for requiring very little sleep. Instead, they depended on the power nap to keep up with the pace. Power napping is an excellent way of refreshing the mind and rejuvenating the ability to process new information. However, you should rest for no longer than twenty minutes, to avoid waking up groggy and dazed.

Make certain you will not be disturbed, unplug any phones, put a DO NOT DISTURB sign on your door, and then find a quiet place to lie down. Now, set your alarm clock to wake you in twenty minutes, close your eyes and direct your mind towards relaxing, non-provocative thoughts.

81

SPICE

Eating curries can be a very tasty way of improving the mind for, as several studies have shown, certain spices used in curry preparation can both sharpen and preserve brain function. Ginger, for example, is believed to harbour certain brain-protective properties, although the most effective spice discovered so far is turmeric, the spice which gives curry its familiar yellow colouring.

Turmeric (of which the key component is curcumin) is a powerful antioxidant which destroys the cell-damaging free radicals. Curcumin also has the ability, according to recent studies, to slow down Alzheimer's disease, which is, perhaps not coincidentally, less prevalent in Asia than on other continents.

You have the morals of a rabbit, the character of a slug, and the brain of a platypus.
CYBILL SHEPHERD, US ACTRESS, 1950–

82

SAD

Many people become more depressed with the onset of autumn and winter, and often this is due to the lack of sunlight. Seasonal Affective Disorder (also known as SAD) can severely impair your mood, affect your sleep patterns and cause general fatigue.

If this sounds familiar to you, whenever possible, try spending as much time in light, bright environments. If you work in an office try moving your desk near a window. Take as many walks outside as you can or take short bike-rides or runs. A specially designed lamp can be purchased that mimics the glow of sunlight and can be timed to gradually increase its light in the morning, fooling your body into thinking it is receiving natural light. Severe cases can be treated with light therapy, but for this you will need to consult with your doctor.

83

KAVA KAVA

Kava kava is yet another member of the natural antidepressant family of plants which also includes ginkgo biloba (page 79) and St John's wort (page 94). In the South Pacific, where kava kava is grown in large quantities, it is frequently made into a special drink which is known to induce a sense of well-being, reduce stress and generally relax both mind and body. In the West, kava kava is often prescribed by alternative practitioners of medicine as a mild anti-depressant and tranquillizer. However, as with all the other 'drugs' described in this book, a doctor's advice should be sought before using kava kava – particularly as it has been known to cause liver problems.

84

ST JOHN'S WORT

As with ginkgo biloba and ginseng, St John's wort has been known for its healing properties for thousands of years, but it is only recently that it has been lauded as an effective, alternative treatment (in contrast to prescription drugs) for mild depression. In this case, the most important compound found in the plant is hypericin, which is an antidepressant and mood stabilizer, and is found at its highest concentration in the bright yellow flowers. However, as with prescription drugs, St John's wort has been known to cause side effects, such as an increased sensitivity to light.

NB – St John's wort should not be taken if you are on any other medication and not without first consulting your doctor.

85

QUIZ 9

Once upon a time, there were three princes who wished to marry a princess. The princess's father, however, was rather conservative, and did not feel she was ready to marry any of them. He therefore decided to give three of them tests that he believed none would be able to pass. First, he blindfolded them all, then led each in turn to his individual test.

The King led the first prince to the base of a mountain where there were ten painted, wooden doors, glistening in the sun. 'All but one of these doors in front of you are white,' said the King. 'If you can tell me within the next ten minutes which door is black you may marry my daughter. You may not speak to anyone, and you may not remove your blindfold.'

The King led the second prince to a hillside, and gazed out across his lush green valleys to the edge of his kingdom, where ten beautiful buildings stood. 'All but one of these buildings in front of you are white,' the King said. 'If you can tell me within the next ten minutes which building is black you may marry my daughter. You may not speak to anyone, and you may not remove your blindfold.'

The King led the third prince to a magnificent dining table where ten places were impeccably laid out. 'All but one of the napkins on this table are white,' said the King. 'If you can tell me within the next ten minutes which napkin is black then you may marry my daughter. You may not speak to anyone, and you may not remove your blindfold.'

Ten minutes later, only one of the princes had successfully identified the black object amongst the white. Which one of the princes had succeeded?

(Answer on page 116)

86

ARTS AND CRAFTS

Yearly holidays are all well and good, but in a world in which our day-to-day spare time is often eaten up by shopping, cleaning and generally rushing around, it can be beneficial to begin a recreational activity such as pottery, painting, jewellery-making or weaving. Not only will this allow you to broaden your horizons and explore the artistic side of your nature, but it is also a wonderful way to relax and free your mind from everyday stresses and strains.

87

AVOID JUNK FOOD

Junk food such as shop-bought hamburgers, hotdogs, fizzy drinks and sweets are packed full of additives and preservatives which can often trigger hyperactivity in children and young adults. Junk foods also contain high levels of unrefined sugar which, while temporarily giving an energy boost, will inevitably be followed by a blood-sugar low that will cause depression and anxiety. Junk food is also frequently high in saturated fats which tend to clog arteries, impairing a good flow of blood to the brain.

88

REMEMBERING NAMES

Nowadays, we will almost certainly meet a huge number of people during the course of our lives. Particularly if you are meeting several new people at once, remembering their names is not easy. One way to help you remember your new acquaintances is to repeat their names as often as possible while you are talking to them (though perhaps not *too* often, otherwise they might think you a bit strange!). Another method is to try to make a mental picture from their name – with, 'Brian Carter' for instance, you could transpose the letters of the first name to come up with 'Brain', and then picture a cart and horse.

Your memory is much more effective when dealing with images, so give it a helping hand!

*All sorts of bodily diseases are produced
by half-used minds.*
GEORGE BERNARD SHAW, IRISH PLAYWRIGHT, 1856–1950

89

REFLEXOLOGY

With its focus on pressure points it is related to acupuncture, but reflexology tends to concentrate more on key pressure points in the feet (and occasionally the hands) in order to balance the body's energy levels. Practitioners follow a map of the foot using their thumbs and fingers to apply pressure to various points that correspond to the different organs of the body. In relation to the mind, reflexology can benefit people who suffer from migraines or who are experiencing insomnia, hypertension or anxiety.

There's no pleasure i' living, if you're to be corked up for iver, and only dribble your mind out by the sly, like a leaky barrel.
(Adam Bede)
GEORGE ELIOT, ENGLISH NOVELIST, 1819–80

90

B VITAMINS

B-complex vitamins are crucial for preventing mild depression and, although found in many common foodstuffs such as whole grains, avocados, mushrooms, seeds, cheese and eggs, it is on occasion advisable to take supplements. In particular, vitamin B6 – which is crucial for the brain to manufacture the required levels of serotonin – is essential for keeping depression at bay.

Which of the following is *not* an anagram of the name of a famous composer?

MET BACH

HAD LEN

PHONIC

GNAWER

IS IRONS

(Answer on page 116)

91

CHANGE YOUR HABITS

According to recent studies we all, in some form or another, suffer from obsessive-compulsive disorder. Thankfully, in most cases this is so mild that it doesn't cause any immediate problems, but in order to improve our minds it can be beneficial to challenge some of the habits we have formed without realizing we have them. For example, most people put a sock on a particular foot first. If you can discover which order you normally do yours then the test is to change this pattern, which in a lot of cases is easier said than done! Other areas to think about might include which tap you turn on first when running a bath – hot or cold? Or which hand you pick up your first cup of coffee with in the morning? Variety is the spice of life, and dusts the cobwebs from the brain.

92

INDIAN HEAD MASSAGE

In India this form of massage has been practised for more than 1,000 years as a means of relieving stress and tension, and, so some say, as a way of increasing hair growth! Whether or not the latter is true, there can be little doubt about the benefits of an Indian head massage to mental and physical well-being.

Concentrating on the head, shoulders, scalp and face, the practitioner massages your skin with a gentle but firm rhythm (often using scented oils) to relax your muscles and unknot any blockages or tension you might have. A good practitioner will also be able to relieve headaches and eyestrain, increase your concentration levels, and boost your energy.

The mind is like an iceberg, it floats with
one-seventh of its bulk above water.
SIGMUND FREUD, AUSTRIAN NEUROLOGIST,
FOUNDER OF PSYCHOANALYSIS, 1856–1939

93

JIGSAWS

As with all the other games and brainteasers contained in this book, jigsaws are a wonderful way of relaxing the mind while at the same time keeping the brain in trim. Try choosing a puzzle of a famous painting – that way you will become familiar with a notable work of art while enjoying the challenge of putting it together!

The mind is but a barren soil; a soil which is soon exhausted, and will produce no crop, or only one, unless it be continually fertilized and enriched with foreign matter.
JOSHUA REYNOLDS, ENGLISH PORTRAIT PAINTER, 1723–93

94

QUIZ 10

If you have read thus far and taken on board at least some of the information provided, then your brain should be able to cope with the following puzzle taken from one of Edward de Bono's excellent books, *The 5-Day Course in Thinking*.

Imagine the following: take three empty bottles with narrow necks and stand them on a solid, flat surface in a triangular formation. Now take four table knives and make certain that the base of each bottle is just over a knife's length in distance from the bases of the other two bottles. Your task is to construct a platform on top of the bottles that is sturdy enough to hold a full glass of water, using only the four knives.

(Answer on page 116)

95

VISUALIZATION

If you have ever doubted that the mind and body are inextricably linked, think of those times when you are most hungry and can't get a certain food out of your mind, such as a big, juicy steak or a large, deep-pan pizza. Just imagining it makes your mouth water or your stomach rumble, showing how a mental image can prompt a physical reaction.

Visualization is simply a positive extension of this reaction. For instance, if you are suffering from a headache or perhaps a pain elsewhere in your body, visualizing the easing and release of that pain can often alleviate your symptoms. First of all, find a comfortable position (lying down is probably the best), loosen your clothing and make sure there are no other distractions. Now, close your eyes and visualize the pain disappearing.

96

BREWER'S YEAST

Although brewer's yeast is not the most obvious choice when faced with improving your mind, it is in fact one of the richest sources of brain nutrients on the market. Containing seventeen key vitamins (including the all-important B vitamins), fourteen minerals and a large amount of amino acids, brewer's yeast is an excellent supplement for boosting the memory. Brewer's yeast is also packed full of key minerals such as magnesium, potassium and chromium, all of which are necessary for keeping the mind alert.

One word of caution, however – do not take brewer's yeast if you suffer from kidney stones or gout.

97

EGGS

Some years ago eggs fell out of favour with nutritionists who were worried about their high levels of cholesterol (which can lead to blocked arteries) – however, recent studies have reported back that the foods we should really avoid are those containing high levels of saturated fats, rather than cholesterol.

In fact, eggs are a particularly good source of tryptophan, which is one of the amino acids required by the brain to produce serotonin. It is best to boil or poach your eggs rather than fry them, as frying will dramatically destroy nutrients and, if you've used oil, will raise your cholesterol.

Imagination is more important than knowledge.
ALBERT EINSTEIN, GERMAN THEORETICAL PHYSICIST, 1879–1955

98

DEEP BREATHING

When told that they aren't making the most of their breathing, the average person will laugh in your face. After all, you breathe in, you breathe out – that's all there is to it, right? Wrong. The way in which you breathe is extremely important, especially when it comes to stress relief.

Stand upright with your legs slightly apart and your arms by your sides. Close your eyes and relax your body. Now, take in one very deep breath, hold it to the count of five and then *slowly* release the breath to another count of five. Repeat this action ten times. Other methods of controlling your breathing include raising your arms out to each side as you breathe in, then releasing them slowly back down to your sides as you breathe out.

Deep breathing provokes a 'relaxation response' – which includes changes in metabolism, heart rate, respiration, brain chemistry and blood pressure.

99

PLUS / MINUS METHOD

Often the simplest, most obvious ways of facing a stressful situation are the best, and the plus/minus method is just such a case.

Firstly, draw up two columns, one headed 'Plus', the other headed 'Minus'. Underneath the Plus column write out all the pros that are relevant to your particular problem and under the Minus column write out all the relevant cons. Now weigh up each column and see which one comes out top.

100

CONCENTRATION

Improving your concentration is crucial to improving your mind. You may have problems with your concentration if any of the statements following apply to you:

- Do you get restless or procrastinate when you're given a task to do?
- Has a task been explained to you, but you've subsequently forgotten how to begin?
- After reading a page do you feel as though you've immediately forgotten what was written?

Following some of the suggestions in this book so far will mean your body and mind are already in training to make a better, healthier brain, but further suggestions include: reduce the distractions around you; make sure you know what your task involves, and de-clutter your work area. Be aware of when your mind wanders, and try to correct the tendency – when we concentrate, we see to the heart of the problem, or situation, which enables us to be much more effective at work and also in our leisure pursuits.

101

ONE MORE

Try to think up a one-hundred-and-second way to improve your mind…

*Clarity of mind results in clarity of passion;
that is why a great mind loves ardently and
sees distinctly what it loves.*

BLAISE PASCAL, FRENCH PHILOSOPHER,
MATHEMATICIAN AND PHYSICIST, 1623–62

ANSWERS

Answers to Quiz 1 – page 7

– The barn's shadow
– A stable
– A dictionary
– A nose
– You can ask either bird this question, 'Which door will the other parrot tell me is Hell?' Whichever door it points out, you select the opposite.
– He's lying. Even though he's lying when he says *everything* he says is a lie, some of the things he says *can* be a lie, and this is one of them.

Answer to question on page 15 – 'PATCH'

Answers to Quiz 2 – page 18

– The order of the offices would be: 1 Sally; 2 John; 3 Chris; 4 Isabel; 5 Lucy; 6 Jill.
The answers are:
1. Office 3
2. Sally

3. Offices 1, 2 and 3
4. John takes over the duties formerly assigned to Jill.

Answer to question on page 28 – all the children are boys.

Answers to Quiz 3 – page 30
– 16 days
– the 24th

Answer to question on page 31 – the letter 'g'

Answers to Quiz 4 – page 40
– Rain
– Sunshine
– Halfway; any further and he would be running *out* of the woods.
– Tomorrow
– The vowels: A, E, I, O, U

Answer to question on page 49 – ambiguous

Answers to Quiz 5 – page 53
– The tractor was driven to the island when the water surrounding it was frozen.
– 40 balls

Answer to question on page 55 – 'strengths'

Answer to question on page 59 – Startling, followed by starting, staring, string, sting, sin, in, and finally 'I'.

Answers to Quiz 6 – page 62
– 1. mosaic; 2. fountain pen; 3. full; 4. chain; 5. dessert; 6. review; 7. root beer; 8. french fries; 9. learn; 10. slogan.

Answer to question on page 66 – the surgeon is the boy's mother.

Answer to question on page 72 – 'rhythms'

Answers to Quiz 7 – page 73
– abscond; defying; fighting; hijack; monopoly; understudy
– 'Indivisibility'
– 'Red in the face'
– Marriage
– 'A mixed bag'

Answer to question on page 81 – 241 Euros

Answer to Quiz 8 – page 85 – 60

Answer to Quiz 9 – page 95
– The first prince succeeded at his test; feeling each
of the doors in turn, the black one was warmer
to the touch than the white ones because it
absorbed more heat.

Answer to question on page 101 – MET BACH
– The others were: Handel; Chopin; Wagner; Rossini

Answer to Quiz 10 – page 105
The first part of the solution is that you only need *three*
out of the four knives. Interleave the blades of three of
the knives so that the blade of each knife goes over the
blade of one of the others and under the blade of the
third – this will effectively lock the blades together; the
finished arrangement should look something like a
three-bladed propeller. Then place this arrangement in
such a way that the handle end of each knife rests on
top of one of the three bottles. The locked blades now
form a platform that will support a glass of water.